Collins Book of
Reptiles

Tom McGowen

Illustrated by Rod Ruth

Collins

Glasgow and London

Text and illustrations reviewed and
authenticated by Hymen Marx
Curator of Reptiles and Amphibians
Field Museum of Natural History
Chicago, Illinois

First published in this edition 1979

Published by William Collins Sons and Company Limited, Glasgow and London

© 1978 RAND McNALLY & COMPANY

Printed in the United States of America
by Rand McNally & Company

Bound in Great Britain

ISBN 0 00 104109 6

First printing, 1978

Contents

The Creatures Called Reptiles

A LITHE legless serpent flowing in mysterious fashion through the grass. A big mud turtle, back and belly housed in a bony shell, plodding along in ungainly step on four feet. A slim lizard with brilliantly colored, winglike flaps of skin outstretched, gliding smoothly from one tree to another. A huge, 20-foot-long, knobbed and gnarled crocodile, lurking motionless in a sluggish brown river. Surely no four creatures could seem more different. Yet all four belong to the class of animals known as reptiles.

What is it that relates these animals to one another? A snake seems more like a worm or an eel than like a crocodile. A long-tailed, sprawl-legged, blunt-nosed lizard looks more like the long-tailed, sprawl-legged, blunt-nosed creature called a salamander than it does like a squat, shell-backed turtle. Yet snake, crocodile, lizard, and turtle are "blood relations," while the others are totally different animals. What makes a reptile a reptile?

To begin with, every reptile has a skeleton. A worm has no skeleton, so no matter how much a worm and a snake may look alike as far as their body shapes are concerned, they are not in the least related.

Secondly, all reptiles are air breathers. An eel, gliding over a sandy sea bottom, may look just like a snake, but it is a fish and can only breathe in water, with gills. Reptiles have lungs that breathe only air, even reptiles such as sea snakes and sea turtles that spend their whole lives in water. So the eel and the snake are two different life forms, despite their likeness of shape.

Thirdly, every reptile has dry skin covered with some form of scales. The salamander, which looks so much like a lizard that it's even called a lizard in some places, is actually the kind of animal known as an amphibian, like a frog or toad. It has a thin, moist skin. The skin is moist because the salamander loses water from its body through it. Most amphibians frequently

8

Black Pond Turtle (India & Southeast Asia)

Flying Lizard

Indian Cobra

Crocodile

(Tiger) Salamander

have to dunk themselves in a pond or river to get water back into their bodies. If they get too dry, they will die. So an amphibian is basically a water animal, and some kinds of amphibians hardly ever leave the water. But the dry, scaly skin of a reptile holds its body water in. It doesn't need water except for drinking. Lizards and salamanders have a very different "machinery" within.

Both amphibians and most kinds of reptiles lay eggs (although some snakes and lizards give birth to live babies). The eggs of amphibians are soft and jellylike. They can easily dry up and never hatch, so they must be laid in water or in wet places. Most baby amphibians hatch in water and breathe with gills, like fish.

But a reptile egg is covered by a hard shell. The shell isn't necessarily hard and brittle like the shell of a hen's egg; it's often leathery or rubbery. But it protects the inside of the egg so that it cannot dry out. A reptile egg can be laid anywhere on the land, even in a dry, sun-drenched desert. And thus, reptiles are creatures of the *land*. Even reptiles that live in the sea must come onto land to lay their eggs.

These, then, are the four main things that make a reptile a reptile—a skeleton; lungs that breathe air throughout its entire life; a dry, scaly skin; and hard-shelled eggs that are laid on land. No matter how different their body shapes may be, all reptiles share these characteristics that set them apart from other kinds of animals.

There are other things, too, of course. Parts of a reptile's skeleton are different from the skeleton of any other animal. And unlike the feathery birds and the furry mammals (but *like* fish and amphibians) reptiles are "cold-blooded." This does not mean their blood is actually cold to the touch. It means that their bodies take on the temperature of the air or water around them. If the air is chilly, the bodies of most reptiles grow stiff, and the animals have difficulty moving. Reptiles frequently bask in the sunshine to warm their bodies so they can move easily. On the other hand, they cannot stay in heat too long or their bodies will become so hot they will die.

Reptiles share the cold-bloodedness as well as some of the outward appearances of amphibians for a good reason. Amphibians were their ancestors.

There were no such animals as reptiles 320 million years ago, but there were plenty of amphibians. The world was a paradise for them. Enormous, swampy forests sprawled across many parts of the earth—hot, damp, and muddy, and dotted with still pools and slow rivers in which many kinds of amphibians thrived. They had plenty to eat—fish, insects, and each other. And they had plenty of moisture in which to lay their eggs. Many of them could venture up onto the land, just as frogs and other amphibians do today, but they always had to return to the water.

But wherever there is an opening, life will move into it. No animals then lived permanently on land except for insects and other many-legged creatures and several kinds of worms. There was plenty of room.

So, some kinds of amphibians began to move out into the open world. Through

Prehistoric Amphibian (Icthyostega)

Dinosaur
(Stegosaurus)

slight changes in their bodies and skin from generation to generation, some of them became able to spend more and more time on the land. They passed this ability on to their babies, and, as millions of years went by, the changes increased, until there were "in-between" creatures living in the swampy forests. They probably still spent a good deal of time in water, but they were laying eggs, tough-skinned eggs, on land.

By about 310 million years ago, the change was complete. A brand new kind of creature was on the scene. It probably looked much like an amphibian, but it had a dry, scaly skin, and it was just a little quicker and smarter. It was strictly a land animal—the first kind of reptile. The earliest reptile yet discovered was a 2-foot-long creature that lived about 300 million years ago. It was named *Romeriscus,* after the scientist Alfred Romer.

As more millions of years went by, the first primitive reptiles began to split off into groups of slightly different creatures. Some stayed in the swampy forests, some moved out onto plains and even deserts. Some "turned around" and went back to the water, becoming adapted to life there.

The first turtles appeared, the first lizards, the first crocodilians, and a great number of other kinds of reptiles, including the dinosaurs, some of which were the biggest creatures that have ever walked on land. This was the great Age of Reptiles, in which scaly-skinned creatures dominated the land, the water—and even the air.

The Age of Reptiles lasted from about 200 million to 70 million years ago, during which time a vast array of reptiles walked and stalked and skittered and soared and swam in all parts of the world. And then, for reasons not yet fully known, there was a dying-off. Many creatures became extinct.

Today, out of all the kinds of reptiles that once ruled the earth, only four groups, or orders, remain. Each order has a scientific name that comes from Greek or Latin words and that may seem difficult at first sight. But each name has a meaning. As a matter of fact, the word "reptile" comes from a Latin word that means "to creep."

The order Crocodilia, as you can guess, contains crocodiles, as well as alligators, caimans, and the gavial. This order's name comes from the name "crocodile," of course, and that name comes from Greek words that mean "pebble worm."

The order Chelonia includes all turtles. And *Chelonia* comes from the Greek word for turtle.

The order Squamata includes both snakes and lizards, which may seem to be two very different things, but aren't really. Snakes are *descended* from lizards; they are lizards without legs. The skeletons of a few kinds of snakes still have little leg bones, showing that snakes come from lizards that gradually lost their legs millions of years ago. The name *Squamata* means "scales."

The last order is Rhynchocephalia. Its name means "beak heads." Only one living reptile is in this order—the tuatara.

So there you have the orders of the reptiles that inhabit the world today—fascinating and often amazing creatures that are left over from the world of long ago!

Crocodilia

Rhynchocephalia

Squamata

Chelonia

Corythosaurus

Phobosuchus

The Crocodile—FROM AN AGE PAST

THE YOUNG *Corythosaurus,* a duck-billed dinosaur with a disklike crest on its head, stood no more than 10 or 12 feet high. It had strayed away from the group of 30-foot adults feeding nearby in the lush, thick forest bordering a swamp. The young dinosaur wandered along the water's edge, perhaps attracted by the nodding brown heads of a great cluster of cattails that rose out of the water. A large, greenish brown log lay partially submerged among the cattails, but the Corythosaurus paid no attention to it.

This was a mistake. For as the Corythosaurus splashed into the shallow water toward the plants, the "log" suddenly came to life. A 50-foot-long body shot forward, and 6-foot-long jaws gaped open, seizing the dinosaur in a vicious grip. In an instant, the Corythosaurus was dragged into the water, the prey of a *Phobosuchus*—an enormous crocodile as fierce and dangerous as any flesh-eating dinosaur of the world of 80 million years ago.

No crocodile of today is as huge as that 50-foot crocodile of long ago. But, in almost every other way, today's crocodiles, alligators, caimans, and the gavial—the reptiles known as crocodilians—look and live just as their ancient cousin did. Watching them and their ways, we can get a good idea of what life was like during that time when most of the earth was a tropical world ruled by great scaly reptiles.

The crocodilians of today need a hot, wet living place just as their ancestors did. They live in the warmest parts of the world, in and around slow-moving rivers, broad swamps, and marshes. Some live on seacoasts. Crocodiles are found in Africa, parts of Asia, and from the southern tip of Florida down to the northern part of South America. Alligators live in the southeastern United States and in grassy swamps in part of China. Caimans, animals much like alligators, are creatures of Central and South America. The gavial lives in India, Pakistan, Bangladesh, and Burma.

All of these reptiles look very much alike. Scientists can tell a crocodile from an alligator or caiman by the way their teeth fit together; in general it can be said that an alligator has a broader snout than a crocodile. The gavial can be easily recognized by its very long, narrow snout.

All crocodilians are completely at home in water. They are all superb swimmers, swimming by tucking their legs against

Alligator

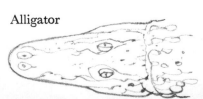

Crocodile

Gavial

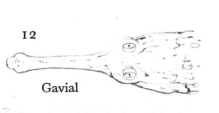

Zebras
CROCODILE

their bodies and wiggling their long, flattish tails. They can also float with only their eyes, nostrils, and ear bumps sticking above the water, which makes it hard for them to be seen. And large crocodilians can stay completely underwater for more than an hour without needing to breathe. They are able to close off their ears and nostrils when they do this.

Most crocodilians usually spend the night in water and come onto land at sunrise to bask in the sun's warmth. To walk on land, a crocodilian lifts its body up off the ground with its legs straight under it and plods along. The gavial doesn't come onto land as often as other crocodilians do; its legs are too weak to do much walking.

The biggest crocodilians of today, such as the Nile crocodile of Africa, are about 20 feet long. An unwary animal of almost any size, including lions, young hippopotamuses, and even buffalo, can become the prey of such a big crocodile. The reptiles lie in wait near a part of the river that is a favorite drinking place for animals. Sluggish and ponderous though a crocodile may seem, it can move surprisingly fast in a quick rush, and many an animal coming to drink may find itself suddenly seized by enormous, grinning jaws. A crocodile may also strike from the water, gliding silent and unseen toward a drinking animal and seizing it by the snout or leg, or sweeping it into the water with a slap of its long tail. Humans, too, have been dragged into the water by those fierce jaws!

Crocodilians cannot chew, so when a crocodile or alligator gets its prey into the water, it *tears* it apart. It does this by holding the animal in the tremendous vise-like grip of its jaws and turning over and over in the water, twisting the prey with such violence that a portion of it comes off in the crocodilian's mouth. The reptile then raises its head out of the water and, with quick jerks, works the piece of meat down its throat. After a few minutes, it goes underwater again to twist off another mouthful of meat.

However, crocodilians do not always prey upon land animals. They often get much of their food—fish and turtles—from the water. And the gavial, although it too sometimes reaches a length of 20 feet or more, eats *only* fish, because that's what its slender jaws, filled with many teeth, are designed to catch. A gavial lying in wait in the water can easily trap fish trying to swim past it, just by swinging its head to the side and snapping its jaws together.

Most land animals are in deadly danger from big crocodiles. However, several kinds of birds are not. The reptiles leave their mouths wide open when they bask, in order to help cool off their bodies. The birds—sandpipers, storks, and others—walk among basking crocodiles, stand next to them, and even climb into the crocodiles' gaping mouths. They are actually *cleaning* the mouths and bodies of the big reptiles, removing leeches and other parasites. Either the crocodiles *want* to have these cleaning jobs done, or else they simply ignore the birds. But, in any event, the birds never seem to be attacked.

All crocodilians hatch out of hard-shelled

Gavial

14

white eggs, about the size of a hen's egg, that their mothers lay on land. But different kinds of mother crocodilians have different ways of laying their eggs. An American alligator scoops up mouthfuls of mud and plants and mixes them together to build a 3-foot-high, dome-shaped nest. She scoops a hollow in the middle of the nest and lays her eggs—anywhere from 20 to 70—in the hollow. Then she covers the eggs with the mud and plant mixture. A Nile crocodile digs a 2-foot-deep pit to lay her eggs in, while some Asian crocodiles use mounds of leaves to make their nests.

After the eggs are laid, the mother waits nearby to defend the nest if necessary. In the heat of the nest, the little crocodilians hatch out, breaking through the egg shells by means of the "egg tooth" each baby has on its mouth. The babies make grunting or peeping noises, and, hearing this, the mother tears open the nest and sets the youngsters free. They follow her about, like ducklings following a mother duck, for a few days, then they are off on their own. Baby crocodilians are in great danger for a long time, because many animals—even larger crocodilians—will gladly eat them.

Most people look upon crocodilians as very frightening and disagreeable creatures. But they are simply wild animals, surviving in their own way. They are really quite *useful,* because they are an important part of the balance of nature. In the South, the American alligator eats gars. Big predatory fish, gars have no major enemy but alligators, and, without the reptiles to keep them in check, they could well wipe out many kinds of fish humans can eat. Holes alligators dig create tiny "ponds" in which, in times of drought, fish can survive and from which many animals can drink. Crocodiles, too, are actually a useful and important part of the plant and animal community where they live.

But in recent years, crocodilians in many places have been ruthlessly killed off by humans—not really because they are dangerous, but simply because their skins can be made into "pretty" belts, shoes, and purses. Nile crocodiles have disappeared from places where they lived for millions of years. Even though some crocodilians can be dangerous to humans, it will be too bad if these big, dinosaurlike creatures are ever wiped out—which could easily happen! In many ways, these animals are like no others, and they give us a glimpse of the world as it once was. If we do not try to preserve them, they could become as extinct as the dinosaurs—and the world would be poorer without them!

The Giant Snake—CONSTRICTOR

IT WAS DUSK and the forest greenery was turning gray in the waning light. A pair of bushbucks, doe and calf, came moving at a sure-footed trot through the dense undergrowth to the water hole at which they were accustomed to drink. They were deerlike creatures, golden furred and graceful. The mother stood some 28 inches high at the shoulders, the calf was about half her size. Their hearing was sensitive and their eyesight keen—but they neither saw nor heard the creature that lay, still as death, beside the water hole.

It had been waiting there, with un-moving patience, most of the day. Its patterned, brownish green body blended perfectly into its surroundings, and it was literally invisible in its shadowed hiding place in the high grass. It was a 20-foot-long African rock python, about to catch a meal.

The bushbucks trotted confidently to the water hole and paused at the edge to drink. The python stealthily rearranged its coils. And as the bushbucks finished drinking and straightened up, the python struck!

Its target was the calf, the animal both closest to it and of a size it could most easily handle. With jaws gaping, the snake's head shot forward, seizing the calf by the neck. The force of the blow knocked the young bushbuck to the ground. At the instant the serpent struck, the mother bushbuck bounded back in instinctive fear. Then she stood, trembling and terrified, to watch. There was nothing she could do to aid her young one.

Crazed with fear, the young bushbuck tried to scramble free of the grip that held it. But the grip was like a vise, and the more the calf tried to pull away, the firmer the python's sharp, backward-curving teeth dug into its flesh!

And so the snake held its captive fast. Now the business of killing the prey had to be done.

The snake's long body began to move. It slid forward over the bushbuck's strug-gling form, slipped beneath it, then curled over it again. Slowly but surely, the python coiled itself around the prey.

The bushbuck's struggles ceased. So tightly were the snake's coils wound around it that it could not move. It could not even breathe. Mouth open, it sought desperately for air. The snake did not *squeeze*, there was no need for that; the tightness of its coils was enough to keep the bushbuck's

Bushbuck

AFRICAN ROCK PYTHON

lungs from expanding. Eyes bulging, the bushbuck ran out of air and it died.

The python remained with its coils wrapped around the dead animal for a time. Then, slowly, the snake began to unwind itself and move into position to feed. The mother bushbuck had long since sadly departed.

The snake's wide open mouth slid forward over the nose of the dead calf. Gently and carefully, the snake worked its way forward. The calf's head disappeared down the snake's throat. Minute by minute the snake continued to move its body forward over the calf, while powerful muscles in its throat helped push the swallowed portion into the snake's body.

The dusk became darkness. The forest was alive with sounds and scents of night creatures, all ignored by the giant snake busy with the slow process of getting the bushbuck into its stomach. In order to swallow the bulkier parts of the animal, the snake's upper and lower jaw actually came apart inside its skin. Its head *stretched* incredibly to make room for the thicker parts of the prey.

After a little more than half an hour, the python had completed its task. It lay with a great swollen lump in the center of its body. It would lie thus, unmoving, for the better part of two weeks while the body of the bushbuck digested. For much of this time, the python would be completely helpless and unable to defend itself. When the meal was finally digested, the python would crawl on its way, not needing to seek food again for many days.

The African rock python, which may reach a length of 32 feet, is one of the world's six giant snakes. The other five are: the boa constrictor, found from Mexico down into much of South America; the anaconda of South America; and the Indian python, reticulated python, and amethystine python—all of which inhabit many parts of Southeast Asia. The biggest of these snakes is probably the anaconda, which some scientists believe may reach a length of 37 feet. The smallest of the giants is the boa constrictor, seldom more than 18 feet in length.

All of the giant snakes share a common trait—the way they get their food. All catch prey with their jaws, then loop their bodies around it in tight coils. Many people believe that a snake such as a python or boa constrictor actually squeezes its prey to death, breaking the animal's bones and crushing it to a pulp, but this is not true. The giant snakes kill their prey by holding it so tightly it cannot breathe.

Just how large a creature can a giant snake swallow? There have been stories of giant snakes swallowing horses and cows, but such a feat would really be impossible for even the biggest of snakes. However, a 20-foot snake, for example, can swallow some surprisingly large creatures, such as goats, sheep, antelope, or most any animal that doesn't weigh much more than a hundred pounds and isn't too broad and bulky. Such things as a goat's horns and hooves, a crocodile's bony, armored skin, and even a porcupine's quills do not bother the snake a bit. It is able to digest them.

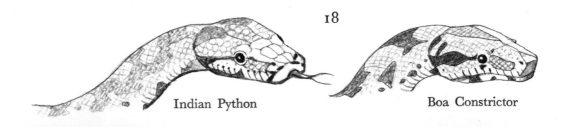

Indian Python   Boa Constrictor

There are also horrible stories of giant snakes eating people, but these stories, too, are untrue. A human would simply be too much of a mouthful for even the biggest snake. However, these big snakes *can* be dangerous to humans. Their mouths are filled with nearly a hundred long, sharp teeth which can inflict terrible wounds. People have been injured and even killed by the bites of big snakes, even though the snakes did not try to eat them.

It would seem as if such a big, deadly creature as a giant snake would be a true "lord of the jungle," with nothing to fear from any other animal. But such is not the case. When giant snakes are young and small, a great many creatures prey on *them*, and even when they are full size, they can still fall prey to other animals. Explorers have seen large crocodiles drag giant snakes into the water and twist them to bits. African hyenas kill and eat fully grown rock pythons. A warthog, a large, heavy beast with 2-foot-long tusks and sharp hooves, was watched as it ripped apart a 12-foot-long African python. And an explorer in India once came across a 17-foot Indian python that had just been killed by a pair of otters, which are fast, smart animals and savage fighters. So giant snakes are not always the slayer; they can become the slain instead.

For the most part, giant snakes are creatures of the night, although several kinds seem to be active during part of the day as well. Like all snakes, they are virtually deaf and cannot see well either, except at close range. However, a snake lying in wait at a water hole can feel through its body the vibrations of the footsteps of approaching animals, and with its keen sense of smell it can detect an animal nearby.

Most of the giant snakes, except for the boa constrictor, are good tree climbers and fair swimmers. However, the champion swimmer is the anaconda, which spends most of its time in the waters of slow-moving rivers. It feeds on some water creatures, such as caimans, which are similar to alligators, but it mainly preys on birds and mammals that come to the river to drink.

The giant snakes are actually just the largest members of a family of numerous snakes known as the Boidae. All the other snakes in this family live and act much like their giant relatives.

Anaconda

The Rattlesnake—PIT VIPER

THE SNAKE did not look at all well. Its colors were dull, its scales had an oddly swollen look, and its eyes were clouded and bluish. It lay motionless, coiled in a secluded hiding place between a low bush and a large boulder.

Days passed during which the snake hardly moved. Then, slowly, its appearance changed. The cloudiness disappeared from its eyes, and they again became golden and catlike. The puffiness of its scales went down. Its color seemed to brighten.

It began to move, pushing its head against the rough side of the boulder, rubbing nose and chin against the rock much as a cat rubs its head against a chair leg. The skin on the snake's nose slowly split from the friction of rubbing. The break widened, and, as the snake continued to rub against the rock, the skin was pushed back over its head.

The snake started to crawl, and as it crawled, the loose skin folded backward, turning inside out, sliding back along the snake's body. As the old skin was pushed off, new skin was revealed, shiny and bright with the tan, yellow, and dark brown of an eastern diamondback rattlesnake.

In minutes, the snake's old skin dragged from the reptile's tail in a single, long piece. As the tail slid over a rough bit of bark, the skin was torn loose and left behind, a pale snake-ghost, to be slowly tattered to shreds by wind and rain.

Resplendent in the bright new skin that had formed beneath the old one, the snake slithered on. It was vigorous, now, and ravenous. The process of molting, shedding its skin, had taken more than 10 days, and during most of that time the snake had not moved from its place of seclusion and had not eaten. Now it sought food.

A red, forked tongue flickered in and out, in and out, of the slit between the lips of its closed mouth. The tongue was a hunting tool. It gathered in scents from the air and carried them to a special place in the snake's mouth. The snake was seeking the scent of warm life—a rat, rabbit, or other living creature that could end its hunger.

It continued to crawl, moving through the night's darkness with a steady, sinuous curving of its body. It was a creature of the night; this was its natural hunting time. Constantly, its tongue flickered, seeking.

Abruptly, the snake found what it sought: the strong scent of an animal close by.

At most other times the rattler would

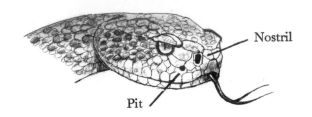

Nostril

Pit

have coiled itself in a good hiding place, waiting for prey to come within reach of it. But now it was driven by its desperate hunger. It crawled in the direction of the scent.

The animal it had scented was a young cottontail rabbit. The rabbit, too, was a creature of the night. It came out to feed and frisk from dusk to dawn, and it lay hidden during the day. It had discovered a patch of tasty clover and was happily munching, unaware of the scaly death gliding silently toward it.

The rabbit was well hidden by the darkness, but this did not matter to the diamondback. It didn't need to see; it had the scent to follow, and when it was within 2 feet of the rabbit it had something else— the *warmth* of the furry creature. The snake knew exactly where the rabbit was.

The diamondback was a good 5 feet long. When it was less than half its body length away from the rabbit, it struck, thrusting itself forward in a quick-as-lightning motion. Its mouth gaped open into nearly a straight line, its two needle-sharp front fangs sprang erect and buried themselves in the rabbit's back. Those two teeth were like hypodermic needles. They were hollow, and a dose of deadly poison squirted through each of them into the cottontail's body.

The snake did not fasten its teeth onto the rabbit; it pulled back an instant after striking. The rabbit gave a single bound as if seeking to escape, then staggered, flopped onto its side, and gave a convulsive shudder. The poison had already done its work.

The diamondback's tongue flickered over the still form as if testing for any last sign of life. Then, positioning itself carefully, the rattler opened its mouth and began to swallow the rabbit headfirst. The snake's fangs now lay flat against the roof of its mouth, out of the way. A little at a time, the snake worked its way forward, sliding its mouth over the rabbit's body, until the furry corpse vanished down its gullet.

The eastern diamondback rattlesnake and all other rattlesnakes are strictly American. Most kinds of rattlers live in North America, but some kinds are also found in Central and South America. None live in any other part of the world.

The thing that makes a rattlesnake different from any other kind of snake is, of course, its rattle. The rattle is a chain of hard, dry, loosely connected shells like hollow rings on the end of the rattler's tail. These shells are actually a kind of scale. A newborn rattlesnake has a small, cone-shaped scale at the tip of its tail. Each time a growing rattler sheds its skin, a new shell is formed inside the old one, pushing it back. Inasmuch as a rattler molts three or four times a year, a two- or three-year-old snake usually has quite a string on its rattle. However, the older shells tend to wear out and fall off, so few rattlers have more than ten or so altogether.

The snake uses its rattle as a warning device. A coiled rattler is usually well hidden and hard to see, and a large creature such as a horse or human might step on it. So the snake lifts its tail and shakes its rattle faster than an eye can see, making

22

a buzzing, whirring noise. "I am here," says that sound, "Look out for me!" The snake's rattle is also a warning to any creature that might attack it. However, a rattlesnake will not *always* rattle a warning—sometimes it will strike without one.

Rattlesnakes belong to the group of snakes known as pit vipers, which includes the copperhead and the cottonmouth. For some people, *pit viper* brings to mind a squirming, hissing snake that lives in a pit, but that isn't what the name means. A pit viper has pits, or openings, on its head—one on each side, between the eye and the nostril, but slightly lower. These pits, like the snake's tongue, are tools for hunting. They detect heat, such as the warmth of a living creature, helping the snake find its prey. A pit viper's pits can "feel" body warmth from as much as 20 inches away; even in total darkness the snake knows exactly where to strike! In experiments by scientists, rattlesnakes have been blindfolded, their nostrils plugged, and then a warm object such as a light bulb covered with cloth or rubber has been put near them. Even though the snakes could not see or smell, they struck at exactly the right place, never missing. On the other hand, when rattlesnakes' pits have been covered up in experiments, the snakes often missed when they struck, even though they could clearly see what they were striking at. Obviously, a rattlesnake's pits are of tremendous help to it in getting its food.

The eastern diamondback rattler gets its name from the pattern of dark brown diamond shapes, edged with yellow, that run the length of its body. It is the biggest of the rattlesnakes, sometimes reaching a length of more than 7 feet, although it is usually only 5 or 6 feet. It lives in the coastal lowlands from Florida to North Carolina in low, brushy country.

Next biggest rattler is the western diamondback, which averages a little more than 5 feet in length. It too has brown, diamond-shaped spots. It is found in dry, open country from Missouri to California, and southward to Texas.

The timber, or banded, rattlesnake lives in the eastern part of the United States, as far north as Maine and as far west as Wisconsin. It is usually a little less than 5 feet long and is banded with tan and dark brown zigzags edged with yellow.

The prairie rattlesnake lives in the western part of the country, just "across" from the territory of the timber rattler. About 3 feet long, it is usually greenish in color, although it has a slightly different look.

The rattlesnake called the sidewinder, because of its sideways gliding method of crawling over sand, is a snake of the deserts of the Southwest. Usually no more than 2 feet long, it is easily recognized by the odd, short "horn" on its nose. This "horn" is really just an oversized scale.

Twenty-nine species of rattlers live in North America, but these five are the best known. They are dangerous reptiles; frequently they do bite humans. But they play a necessary part in keeping down the number of rats, rabbits, and other creatures that might otherwise multiply too greatly and cause humankind serious problems.

Sidewinder

The Cobra—HOODED SERPENT

A LEOPARD was prowling through the high grass of an African plain, seeking an antelope or other animal to satisfy its hunger. Unfortunately for the leopard, its stealthy pace was carrying it straight toward a creature it would not particularly care to meet—and a creature that did not much care to be disturbed. The creature felt the tread of the approaching cat coming closer, and this meant the possibility of danger. It prepared to defend itself.

When the leopard was no more than 8 feet away, the creature took action. The leopard was confronted by the upper portion of a 6-foot-long, dull black snake, with a tan and black striped throat, rearing above the grass. A narrow, dome-shaped "hood" spread out behind the serpent's head. There was a quick hiss and a glittering stream flew from the reptile's mouth directly into the startled cat's eyes.

The leopard gave a yowling shriek of pain and did a somersault backward into the grass. Its eyes burned as if they were afire, and it could not see! It rolled in agony, trying to rub away the pain with its paws. Meanwhile, the snake dropped back into the grass and zigzagged rapidly off.

The leopard had had the bad luck to encounter a spitting cobra—a poisonous snake able to squirt its poison in two streams for a distance of nearly 10 feet toward the eyes of an enemy. The snake does this only to defend itself, and while its victim is helpless it makes its escape. It is able to "spit" quickly, a number of times if necessary, for the poison has no effect unless it touches an opponent's eyes. Then it burns horribly, causing blindness that only slowly wears away.

The spitting cobra does not use its poison only in defense. It uses it mainly just as any other poisonous snake does—to kill, by biting, the creatures that are its food.

Cobras are members of a large family of snakes, the elapids, found in every part of the world except Europe. Only a few kinds can "spit," but all are poisonous, and two are the most poisonous of all snakes.

One of those two is probably the most widely feared snake in the world, not only because of its deadly bite, but because of the terror of its appearance. For it is a *giant* snake, the longest of all poisonous snakes—the dreaded king cobra. It lives in India, southern China, and parts of Southeast Asia.

The king cobra is truly a giant. Usually

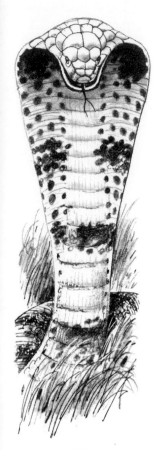

King Cobra

about 13 feet long, it may even reach a length of 18 feet or more. And it *is* deadly. A human can die from its bite within 15 minutes. Fortunately, it seldom attacks a human unless it feels that it or its eggs are in danger. Usually, it avoids people. Its favorite home and hunting ground is thick jungle where it finds its main food—other snakes. For the king cobra eats mostly all kinds of snakes, including even poisonous snakes.

The king cobra has a yellowish or olive brown body, with a yellowish chin and throat. Coiled, or crawling in search of prey, it looks much like any other kind of snake. But when it is angry or startled, it rears up and spreads its "hood." It does this by lifting some of its movable ribs so that the skin over them is stretched out—like an umbrella opening up. This forms the oval hood behind its head, which is the "trademark" of cobras. Some scientists think a cobra's hood is a kind of protection, making it hard for another creature to bite the snake's neck.

In the same parts of the world where the king cobra is found lives its close relative, the common cobra, which is usually about 6 or 7 feet long. The common cobra is actually more dangerous than the king cobra—not because it is more poisonous, but because it does not avoid people as the king cobra does. Its main food is rats, and inasmuch as a great many rats live among people, in villages and cities, the snake often goes where rats are—even into houses. Thus, every year, thousands of people in India and other parts of Asia are bitten by

these snakes they just happen to "bump into!" Luckily, the bite of a common cobra does not always cause death. Most people recover from it.

The common cobra also spreads a hood when excited or angry, but its hood is wider and rounder than that of the king cobra. And the common cobra's hood has a design on the back that looks somewhat like a pair of eyeglasses. Because the skin of the hood is spread so thin, light shows through it and the design can be seen from the front, like a pair of big eyes on each side of the cobra's head. Some kinds of cobras have a hood marking that looks like a single big eye.

The snakes called kraits, living in many parts of Southeast Asia, are members of the same family. They are shiny black and from 3 to 6 feet long. Some are marked with yellow or white bands, some have yellow or red heads. Like king cobras they eat mostly other snakes, including their cobra relatives. They are highly poisonous, and their bite can kill a human in a matter of hours. However, kraits do their hunting at night, and are very slow moving and practically harmless in daylight, when they almost never bite. In fact, a scientist once saw a group of Vietnamese children *playing* with several kraits in bright sunlight!

Many members of the elapid family live in Africa. One is the Egyptian cobra, also called an asp. It is about 6 feet long and has a heavier body than its Asian cousins. It is said that the Egyptian queen Cleopatra committed suicide by letting one of these creatures bite her!

The African snakes called mambas be-

26

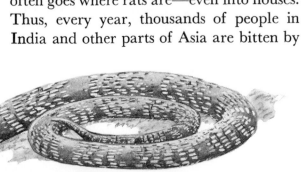

Common Cobra

long to this family. They are long and slender and probably the quickest moving of all snakes. The biggest of them is the famous and feared black mamba, which may be over 13 feet long. It is not truly black, but more of a slate gray or brownish gray. Its bite is fatal. The smaller green mamba lives in the trees, where it hunts among the branches for birds and tree-dwelling frogs and lizards. It, too, is poisonous, but it generally hides from people.

There are members of the elapid family in North and South America, too. They are the brightly colored, medium-sized snakes known as coral snakes. Depending on how you want to look at it, a coral snake has either a red body with broad black bands, or a black body with broad red bands. The bands always have a narrow yellow or whitish ring on each side of them. That combination of colored bands and rings means danger! About half the people bitten by coral snakes die within 24 hours! Most coral snakes are from 18 inches to about 3 feet in length. They hide by day and come out at night to hunt for smaller snakes and lizards, their main food. They poison their prey by chewing on it for a few moments, and when the poison makes it unable to move, they swallow it down.

Cobras even have relatives in the sea—real sea serpents that live for the most part in shallow water near the coasts of Asia and Australia, although they're sometimes found far out in deeper water. They eat mostly fish and eels, which they disable with poison just as a cobra kills its prey on land.

The largest sea snakes are about 6 feet long. These creatures are shaped rather differently from land snakes. Their bodies are flatter, more like the body of a fish or eel, and they have paddle-shaped tails. Some kinds have a thick and bulgy middle and a very thin neck and head. Some sea snakes come onto land to lay their eggs and bask in the sun. Other kinds never leave the water and are almost unable to move if put on land; their babies are born directly from the mother's body into the water.

Cobras and the other members of the family inject poison into prey through their two front fangs just as rattlesnakes do, but not in quite the same way. A cobra's fangs do not lie flat as a rattler's do when its mouth is closed; cobra fangs are shorter and always stick straight down. When the snake strikes, it curls back its snout so that the fangs are bared, and when they pierce the prey, squirting out poison, the cobra usually hangs on and *chews* for a few moments. The cobra's poison is also of a different kind from that of the rattlesnake—but, in the end, it does exactly the same job!

Coral Snake

'Sea Snake

The Freshwater Turtle—PET AND SNAPPER

IT WAS LATE afternoon on a day in early summer. Sunlight slanted through the trees in a patch of forest somewhere in the midwestern United States. A stream ran through the woods, and at one place in the stream a gray log stuck up out of the water. And on the log, all in a row, sat four painted turtles sunning themselves.

They were little creatures, with shells no more than 5 inches long. The name "painted turtle" was a good one—they looked as if they had been decorated by an artist. Bright yellow and orange stripes ran down their necks, orange designs were all around the edges of their brown shells, and splotches of orange colored their legs.

Suddenly, something startled them. Perhaps it was the vibration of human footsteps in the woods nearby, for, although the turtles had no ears, they could feel the sound vibrations through either air or water. So, *plop—plop—plop,* off the log and into the water went the little creatures. After a few moments, their bright heads began to poke up to see if everything was alright. If it was, they would clamber back onto the log to resume their sunbath.

Whereas most people fear crocodilians, hate snakes, and don't care much for lizards,

it seems almost everyone likes turtles. And probably the best-known and best-liked turtles come from the family usually known as freshwater turtles. Painted turtles are members of this family, and you often see them and some of their relatives in pet shops. One relative, the spotted turtle, has bright yellow flecks scattered all over its head and shell, as if someone had shaken a paint-filled brush over it. The red-eared turtle has yellow stripes on its head and neck and a bright patch of red on each side of its head. These three turtles live in North America but have relatives, such as the English pond turtle, in all parts of the world. They spend most of their time in the water, usually only come out to sun themselves on a rock or log, and generally come ashore only to lay their eggs. These reptiles eat all their food underwater, feeding on insects, small fish, tadpoles, and water plants.

Some slightly different kinds of small turtles also live in streams and rivers in North America, but they're not quite as popular as the pond or freshwater turtles. One is called the musk turtle, getting its name from the musky, skunklike odor it gives off when it fears danger. Because of

Spotted Turtle

PAINTED TURTLE

Musk Turtle

this smell the turtle is known as "stinkpot" and "stinking jenny" in many places.

The musk turtle has a large, yellowish brown shell covering its whole body. The shell of a full-grown stinkpot may be 4 inches long. This turtle, too, spends most of its time in the water, crawling about on the river bottom, foraging for insects, worms, tadpoles, snails, small fish, and just about anything else, including dead creatures. It does useful work in helping dispose of a river's "garbage."

Any of the freshwater turtles would make good pets. It is harmless little creatures such as these that make turtles so likeable. But what many people don't know is that not all turtles *are* likeable—some are big, fierce, and dangerous!

The snapping turtle lives in rivers and ponds in the southern United States. It's a large, heavy reptile that may weigh as much as 50 pounds and have a shell 15 inches long. Actually, its body is much too large for its shell, and it can't pull its legs, head, or spiky tail into the shell as many other turtles can. But the snapping turtle doesn't really need such a defense, for few if any creatures would care to tackle it. In fact, most creatures need a defense against *it,* for it will go after most anything that swims—fish, frogs, ducks, geese, other turtles, young muskrats, and even *humans,* who have had toes bitten off by these fierce reptiles!

A snapping turtle attacks from below, coming up underneath its prey and striking like a snake, stretching out its long neck in a quick motion and seizing its meal with a snap of its powerful jaws. Then the prey is torn to pieces with the turtle's sharp claws and vicious jaws. The pieces are swallowed whole, for the snapper, like all turtles, has no teeth and cannot chew.

The snapping turtle sometimes hunts on land, and few creatures are safe from it there, either. It will even attack a snake, catching it behind the head with a quick thrust and biting through its neck. The snapper is truly an ugly and dangerous customer!

And the snapping turtle has a relative that's even bigger and uglier than it is! This creature, the alligator snapping turtle, has a completely different way of capturing prey.

Imagine you're at the bottom of a river somewhere in Florida. Near you, a fish is swimming.

The fish is curious. It has noticed movement in the glistening brown mud where the sloping riverbank merges with the bottom of the river. Something pink is wiggling attractively there—apparently a fat worm, squirming in the mud.

Another wiggle of pink. The fish moves closer to investigate. There does not seem to be any danger. The place where the worm is moving is a small, shallow pit in the mud; there is no sign of anything else in it and no sign of any larger fish or other dangerous enemy nearby. All the fish has to do, it seems, is dart into the pit, snap up the worm, and flit out again.

What the fish has not noticed is the pair of muddy brown *eyes,* with beady black centers, watching it from each side of the

Snapping Turtle

"pit." With a flick of its tail, the fish glides in. Immediately the scaly, mud-colored jaws forming the sides of the "pit" snap shut. For the pit is a *mouth*—the mouth of an alligator snapping turtle!

An alligator snapping turtle is a large, big-headed reptile that weighs as much as 150 pounds and has a shell as much as 2 feet long and 20 inches wide. It lives in rivers and swamps in parts of the southern United States, and it gets most of its food by burying its mud-colored body in the mud on the river bottom and lying in wait with its mouth open. The inside of its mouth resembles wet, glistening mud, and its tongue is split into two branches with fat, pink tips. When the turtle moves its tongue, this "lure" wiggles like a worm writhing in the mud—a sight few fish can resist. The turtle is able to lie on the river bottom for several hours before having to come up for air.

An alligator snapper isn't much of a swimmer, and when it isn't lying in wait it may go lumbering along the river bottom looking for all the world like one of the prehistoric armored dinosaurs called anky-losaurs. Its big shell has three rows of pointed bumps along its length, and its long tail drags behind it in the mud.

So, you see, there are turtles and there are turtles. Some are small, harmless, and likeable—but some *definitely* are not!

If you live in a place where summers are warm and winters cold, and where turtles can be seen in the summer, you may wonder what becomes of them in the winter. After all, they are reptiles, and reptiles are cold-blooded creatures needing warmth and sunshine.

Turtles living in northern areas *hibernate* during the cold wintertime. They dig down into the mud of a marshy place or river bottom or burrow beneath leaves. Slowly, as the cold grows greater, their bodies "slow down." They barely breathe and their hearts barely beat. They are almost—but not quite—dead!

In spring, the sun rises higher in the sky each day. The days grow warmer. Finally the temperature is high enough so the turtles' bodies begin to warm up again. Slowly and sluggishly at first, they begin to rouse, to dig themselves out of their winter quarters, and to come out into the warming-up world.

Alligator Snapping Turtle

31

The Tortoise—TURTLE OF THE LAND

THE ISLAND certainly wasn't much to see. The shore was gray, barren, a gnarled landscape graced here and there with thorny shrubs and cracked with numerous crevices. The party of Spanish sailors, sent ashore from the ship riding at anchor in the bay, picked their way toward a distant line of greenery, cursing from time to time as they stumbled on the uneven ground.

Many minutes later, as they neared the trees, the officer in command stopped short and stared. "By all the saints, look at that!" he exclaimed.

A creature was moving toward them, a creature such as they had never before seen. It was obviously a turtle, but *what* a turtle! Its shell was as wide and deep as the great soup cauldron that served the whole crew! Its legs were like those of an elephant, covered with wide scales that looked like pebbles. It was an immense creature and must have weighed hundreds of pounds. Even though it moved with ponderous slowness, the officer half drew his sword, not sure whether such a huge, scaly reptile might not be dangerous.

But when the reptile caught sight of the humans, it too stopped short. It let out its breath with a hissing sigh and pulled its

head into the safety of its shell. Then it tucked its huge, armored legs into the shell, knees touching, so that the shell's opening was completely blocked. Its back legs, too, were pulled into the shell. It lay there on the barren ground, looking like a misshapen, gray green boulder. The creature depended upon its shell and pebble-scaled skin to protect it against these invaders of its domain.

Such a scene might well have taken place several hundred years ago when Spanish seamen first came to the particular group of islands that lie on the equator, west of the coast of South America. The Spaniards found so many of the giant turtles that they gave the group of islands the name *Galapagos,* which in their language means "tortoise"—the Tortoise Islands. Tortoise is the name for any kind of turtle that lives only on land.

When the Spaniards first came to the Galapagos Islands, the number of giant tortoises they found was incredible. One seaman of long ago wrote that sometimes so many of the creatures swarmed the beach that, if you wanted to go from one part of the sand to another, you had to walk across the tortoises' backs! But for

32 GALAPAGOS TORTOISE

hundreds of years, sea captains of many lands stopped off at the islands to pick up tortoises as fresh meat for their crews. And today the tortoises are almost completely gone. Only about 2,000 of several species are left, scattered among the island group. Most are found on only two of the islands.

Galapagos tortoises are the biggest members of the turtle family except for some of the sea turtles. An old adult Galapagos tortoise may have a shell as much as 4½ feet high and may weigh close to a good 500 pounds.

These creatures are among the longest living of all animals—and they look it, with their wrinkled, scaly skins. There is an authentic record of one Galapagos tortoise, kept as a pet, that lived for at least 152 years. It is suspected that some of these creatures reach an age of 200 or more!

The tortoises of the two islands are a bit different from one another. Those living on the island of Santa Cruz have broad, sloping shells that do not permit the reptiles to raise their heads very high, and these tortoises eat low-growing plants.

The tortoises on the island of Española have high-backed shells that enable the reptiles to stretch their necks to feed on plants that grow high above the ground. Scientists believe this shows how each kind of tortoise has evolved to fit the conditions on the island where it lives.

The tortoises spend their nights sleeping in mud puddles when possible, with just the tops of their heads and shells above water. This keeps mosquitoes from getting at them. By day, the tortoises wander about, moving at a speed of some 4 miles an hour, eating plants and drinking large quantities of water. They trudge back and forth from the forested highlands onto the gray beaches by regular paths, and, because so many millions of tortoises have followed those paths during millions of years, the paths are worn smooth into the rock by the rubbing of the tortoises' plastrons, or belly shells.

The Galapagos tortoises can no longer be hunted, as they are under the protection of the government that owns the islands. And because of their size and armor, the reptiles themselves haven't much to fear from other animals on the islands. But their eggs are in constant danger from wild dogs and other animals that dig up the eggs and eat them. The future is uncertain for these big, harmless reptiles, even though scientists are trying to help them survive.

There are about 50 different kinds of tortoises living in most of the warmest parts of the world, although none of the others are nearly as big as the Galapagos tortoises. Nor do all tortoises live the same sort of life as a Galapagos tortoise.

The gopher tortoise is a brown-shelled reptile, about a foot long, living in dry lands in parts of the southern United States. Like its namesake, the gopher, it is a digger that makes underground tunnels as much as 30 feet long, digging with its two shovellike front feet. At the end of the tunnel there is a larger chamber where the turtle spends its nights. It comes out to wander about during the day, eating grass, leaves, and plant stems.

34

Gopher tortoises seem to like one another's company, for a number of them will usually have their burrows in the same area, 20 or 30 feet apart. Furthermore, two tortoises will often share the same burrow. It isn't known whether these two are mates, a pair of bachelors, or both females. A number of other animals, such as cockroaches, gopher frogs, and toads, often share a gopher tortoise's home.

It is an amazing fact that the little, foot-long gopher tortoise can carry a full-grown person on its back! The person must stand balanced on the shell, but the turtle can slowly plod along, bearing even a 200-pound human with no apparent difficulty!

The gopher tortoise has a close relative that is a desert dweller and is known as the desert tortoise. It, too, digs long tunnels for itself, and it spends its days there, hidden away from the fierce heat of the desert above. It comes out at night to feed mainly on desert plants, which provide it with both food and water.

But the desert tortoise's tunnel is more than a home. It is also a place of refuge from danger. When threatened by an enemy, a desert tortoise will try to scuttle into its tunnel, and there it will brace itself in, pushing its shell up against the roof and its feet against the sides. It is almost impossible for any creature to pull it out.

Desert tortoises don't seem to be quite as friendly toward each other as gopher tortoises are. When two male tortoises meet, they are likely to fight. First they nod their heads rapidly at one another, then they charge, bumping together violently. The purpose of the fight seems to be to see which tortoise can knock the other over onto its back. The loser struggles to turn himself rightside up again, rocking back and forth, twisting his neck and legs, until he manages to get back on his feet.

A great many kinds of tortoises live in Africa. Most are not much different from the gopher or desert tortoise, but one kind is quite different. It has a rather *soft,* flat shell that somewhat resembles a pancake and so is known as the pancake tortoise. Unlike other tortoises, this tortoise can't depend on its shell for protection, so it has worked out a special means of defense. It lives in very rocky country, and when danger threatens, it runs, with surprising speed for a member of the turtle family, to the nearest crevice in the rocks and wedges itself in. Its soft shell is an advantage there, because it allows the tortoise to squeeze into a very thin space. The reptile can only be pulled out of its refuge with the greatest difficulty, and so it simply stays put until the predator leaves. Then the pancake tortoise works itself out and goes on its way again.

35

Desert Tortoises

The Sea Turtle—STRUGGLE FOR SURVIVAL

SHE has been swimming steadily for days, driven by a powerful inner urge that sweeps all else aside. She seldom goes ashore, but now she must hurry to a special place on the land, an island beach far from her regular seacoast home. On that island, she and many others of her kind began their lives, and she is returning now, a journey of some 1,400 miles, to give life—or at least a chance for life—to a new generation. She is a female green turtle, a sea turtle, on her way to lay her eggs.

She surges steadily onward, with a continuous rowing movement of her big front flippers. As she draws nearer to the island, she meets other green turtles, males and females, all heading toward the island. Soon a great number of the big reptiles fill the sea for many miles.

It is daylight when the female comes in sight of the island, and she and the others who have come to lay their eggs wait until the sun sets, for they will die if they stay ashore too long in sunlight, and the task ahead will take a long time.

When darkness lies over the sea and shore, the female swims to the beach. She lies in the surf for a time, peering this way and that, for while she is relatively safe in the water, there is danger to her on land from several kinds of creatures. At last, she hauls herself onto the sand, silver in the moonlight. Slowly she begins to climb toward higher ground, to a place the water will not reach even at high tide. On both sides of her the beach is dotted with the black shapes of other female turtles, all moving toward higher ground.

Movement on land is tremendously difficult for the turtle. Out of the water her heavy, 4-foot-long shell is a crushing weight, but she must keep her 400-pound body raised high enough off the ground so that she can breathe, for if she should try to crawl with her flat bottom shell pressed against the sand, her own weight would squeeze against her lungs and keep them from working. She moves by thrusting her big front flippers ahead and then dragging her body forward, pushing with her hind flippers. Every few feet she stops and emits a great, heaving sigh. Tears are streaming from her eyes! Actually, this is her body's way of getting rid of salt taken in by eating and drinking, but it looks as if she is weeping with exhaustion and effort! She leaves a deep, ridged pattern of tracks behind in the sand.

Female Green Turtle Laying Eggs in Sand

When she finds a spot that seems right, she sweeps at the sand with all four flippers until she has made a shallow pit into which her whole body fits. Then, using her back flippers, she scoops out a hole about 2 feet deep in the bottom of the pit. Into this hole she slowly drops about a hundred whitish, hard-shelled eggs, the size and shape of ping-pong balls.

Easing herself up out of the pit, she shovels sand into it with her back flippers, covering the eggs. She scatters sand in all directions to hide the nest's outline. Then, slowly, with more pauses and more sighs, she makes her way back to the water. She will return again, several more times, to other parts of the beach to dig more nests and lay more eggs—about 500 eggs in all. And she will mate with some of the male turtles waiting out in the water offshore, so that, in several more years, she will come back, her body once again carrying eggs to be laid.

And so, her clutch of eggs lies hidden beneath the sand, waiting to hatch. Many scores of other hidden nests dot the beach on all sides of hers. They are hidden—but far from safe. A prowling monitor lizard discovers the nest next to hers and digs it up, eating the eggs. Many other nests are discovered by other creatures.

Each day the sun bakes down onto the island beach. At the bottom of the nest, where the eggs are piled, there is constant warmth. In about 60 days, the warmth helps hatch the eggs, and the baby turtles break out of their shells. When all have hatched they form a squirming, wiggling pile. Some begin to claw their way up through the sand, seeking more room. Others follow. The nest seems suddenly to erupt, a volcano of tiny turtles no bigger than silver dollars spewing up out of the sand.

Unerringly, the babies begin to scramble toward the sea. They are sent in that direction by a compulsion imprinted in their bodies that drives them toward the greatest open space—the broad sky over the sea.

Many never reach the water. Birds have gathered to await the hatching, and there are many other creatures for which the little turtles with their still-soft shells are easy prey. Some are seized by crabs. Several are swallowed by snakes. Many are picked up and carried away dangling from the beaks of gulls.

A few of the little turtles get to the sea, but there, too, they are still in deadly danger. Most are gulped down by fish. Out of all the hundreds of thousands of baby turtles that manage to hatch from all the undestroyed nests, only a *very* few survive to become adults. Most simply become a meal for some other creature.

Green turtles are the biggest members of a whole family of sea turtles. These reptiles are all much alike in their way of life. They live in the warmer parts of the ocean and never come onto land except to lay their eggs. Only the green turtles, at times, will crawl up onto sandbars to bask for a while in the sunlight.

The green turtle, which gets its name from the greenish color of its flesh, has a yellowish or brownish shell with a touch of

Gulls

Monitor Lizard

Hawksbill Turtle

Loggerhead Turtle

olive. It eats mainly ocean plants, such as the seaweed called turtle grass. Another member of the family, the loggerhead turtle, is slightly smaller than the green turtle, and its shell is usually reddish brown. It eats mostly shellfish and barnacles, as well as fish, sponges, and jellyfish. The loggerhead's taste for jellyfish is strange, for jellyfish have poisonous stinging cells in their tentacles and bodies. This does not seem to bother a loggerhead a bit.

The hawksbill turtle, as its name suggests, has a rather birdlike beak. Its 3-foot-long shell is a golden yellow with reddish brown and deep brown markings. The hawksbill eats some sea plants, together with sponges, sea urchins, and jellyfish.

The Atlantic and Pacific ridley turtles are the smallest members of the family, with shells about 2 feet long. The Atlantic ridley's shell is dark gray or grayish brown; the Pacific ridley has an olive or greenish white shell. Ridley turtles eat mainly small shrimps and crabs.

Another kind of sea turtle, the leatherback, is different from these others and does not belong to their family. The other sea turtles, with horny shells, have a "conservative" look, but the leatherback has a streamlined and almost "futuristic" appearance. Instead of a horny shell, its shell is covered with black or dark brown leathery skin, and it has seven equally spaced ridges running down its length.

The leatherback is probably the best swimmer of all the sea turtles. It almost seems to fly through the water, using its long front paddles like wings. It is the largest of all turtles on land or sea. A full-grown leatherback may weigh a thousand pounds and have a shell more than 6 feet long.

Although sea turtles can't pull their heads or legs into their shells, their large size protects them from most sea creatures except killer whales and large sharks. But the sea turtles have one enemy that has brought several of their kind close to extinction. That enemy is humans.

For many years, people have gone to the places where sea turtles come to mate and lay their eggs, robbing the nests and killing turtles for their meat and shells, some of which are made into tortoiseshell jewelry and rims for eyeglasses. At mating times, the water near those places swarms with turtles that can easily be harpooned, and the female turtles on the beach are totally helpless before a human. Countless millions of eggs are taken from nests each year. And so, green turtles, hawksbills, ridleys, and leatherbacks—plentiful in the world's seas for tens of millions of years—are now becoming rare.

Most of the governments that own the places where the turtles lay their eggs have now taken some steps to protect the turtles, and many scientists are seeking ways of helping them survive. But in spite of laws and in spite of pleas, much of the killing of sea turtles and robbing of their nests still goes on. Scientists and people who care about the wildlife of the world are fearful that someday soon these interesting sea-going reptiles may be gone from the world forever.

39

Leatherback Turtle

The Monitor—GIANT LIZARD

BENEATH a glaring sun, on a dry plain dotted with clumps of small bushes, two big reptiles faced one another. From the tips of their tails to the ends of their long snouts they were both nearly 6 feet in length. Their slender bodies were yellowish brown, flecked with many black spots. Two male Bengal monitor lizards.

With mouths open and throats puffed up, they hissed at one another; one in warning, the other in defiance. "This is my territory," meant the warning hiss, "I will fight to drive you from it!" "I will fight to stay here," was the meaning of the hiss of defiance.

Abruptly, one of the reptiles rose to his hind legs, and the other did likewise. They hurled themselves at each other and began to grapple like two wrestlers, each wrapping his front legs around the other's body. Surprisingly, neither tried to bite or tear the other with its sharp teeth and claws. They merely swayed back and forth in a dance-like struggle.

Then, one managed to hook a back leg around the back leg of the other. At the same moment, he gave a hard shove with his body. The other was knocked backward onto the ground.

The fallen lizard was up in an instant, returning to the fight. Again, the two creatures wrestled with their front legs locked around one another's bodies. Then, again, the same reptile was thrown to the ground by his slightly bulkier opponent.

That was enough. With a last sullen hiss the twice-thrown lizard turned and scuttled away, acknowledging defeat. The "owner" of the territory had successfully defended his domain.

Big male monitor lizards often have combats such as this over territory. Neither lizard is particularly hurt; one simply establishes mastery over the other. However, should two monitors fight over food, things are very different. Then claws and teeth *are* used, and blood is shed.

Monitors are a large family of lizards. All family members are quite alike except for in size and coloring. Different kinds live in the warmer parts of Africa, Australia, Indo-Australia, and Asia. Some monitors are the largest of all lizards—giants ranging in body length from 5 to 10 feet.

Most animals are adapted, or suited, to a particular way of life in a particular place. For example, crocodiles are seldom out of sight of water and could not climb a

tree, while a tree-dwelling chameleon hardly ever comes down to the ground and would not swim. But most monitors seem able to do almost anything—climb trees, swim rivers, run upon the ground, and dig burrows. They all have rather long, slender bodies, and darting, snakelike forked tongues. These tongues are used in hunting to pick up scents of other animals, which is also how snakes use their tongues. Monitors are similar to snakes in a number of ways, and scientists believe both are probably descended from the same kind of lizard ancestor.

The largest of the monitors is a true giant—the famous Komodo dragon lizard that lives on the island of Komodo and several other small islands in Indonesia. A male Komodo dragon lizard may reach a length of 10 feet and weigh as much as 300 pounds. This is a fearsome-appearing reptile, with brownish yellow skin covered with pebblelike scales and creased with heavy folds, like pleats. Looking at one of these creatures, you can't help but think that some dinosaurs must have had skin much like it.

A Komodo dragon lizard will eat the dead body of any creature it finds, but it is also a fierce hunter of live prey. A dragon lizard will often lie in a hiding place beside a trail down which deer or wild pigs are sooner or later bound to come. When a victim is near enough, the dragon lunges at it, seizing the animal with its mouth and dragging it to the ground. It may often slam the animal violently against the earth as if to stun it. Then, with sharp claws and teeth with sawlike edges, it will tear the creature to death. It feeds by ripping off chunks of the prey and gulping them down—flesh, hair, bones and all. It often will use one of its front feet to push an extra-large chunk down its throat.

Komodo dragons are savage and dangerous creatures in the wild. But, surprisingly, these big, fierce, dinosaurlike reptiles can become quite tame and "lovable" when kept in zoos! Some have learned to recognize their keeper and even to come when called by the names they have been given. Even more incredible: two Komodo dragons at the London zoo became so affectionate toward humans that they allowed themselves to be patted like dogs; they were so trustworthy, small children could safely ride on their backs! On the other hand, wild Komodo dragons have been said to attack humans.

Smaller Komodo dragons of up to 4 or 5 feet are good tree climbers, but the larger lizards are too heavy to manage such a feat. However, large and small dragons dig burrows for themselves with their powerful claws, spending nights and hot periods of the day in them.

The second largest monitor is the water monitor, found in many parts of Southeast Asia. It reaches a length of 8 or 9 feet. As its name shows, this big lizard is completely at home in the water of sluggish rivers. It swims like a crocodile, tucking its legs against its body and wiggling its flattish tail, and it can stay underwater for a surprisingly long time. Yet it often leaves the water to climb a tree and lie on a long branch,

42

basking in the sunshine. Like the Komodo dragon, it eats any kind of animal food it can get, live or dead. But, spending as much time in water as it does, it feeds mainly on water creatures—fish, frogs, and turtles, which it swallows whole, shells and all.

Next largest monitor is the parenty monitor of Australia, which reaches a length of 7 feet. A number of other monitors reach a length of 6 feet. One of these is the Nile monitor of Africa, which lives along parts of the Nile River.

The Nile monitor, as much at home in water as the water monitor, can stay underwater for as long as an hour. But it, too, is equally at home on land and can climb trees.

In addition to the live or dead animals they eat, all monitors seem to have a great fondness for eggs, which they usually swallow whole. They raid the nests of birds and turtles, and Nile monitors raid the nests of crocodiles. Of course, raiding a crocodile's nest can be dangerous, because mother crocodiles guard their nests well, and a large crocodile is one of the few creatures able to overcome a big monitor lizard. However, this doesn't stop the Nile monitors. They uncover the eggs and carry them off, one at a time, to a hiding place to enjoy them.

An English game warden once saw two Nile monitors work as a "team" to rob a crocodile's nest. One lizard lured the mother crocodile into chasing it into the river, and the other monitor then dug open the nest and began to feast. Shortly, the other member of the monitor team returned and joined in. When the enraged mother crocodile reappeared, the two lizards trotted off, each carrying one last egg in its mouth.

All female monitors lay eggs, usually in holes they dig, fill with their eggs, then cover up and pack down in order to keep *their* eggs from being found and stolen. But mother Nile monitors have worked out a foolproof way of protecting their eggs. They find a termite nest that has been softened by rain and tear a hole in the side of it. In every termite nest there is a large central chamber, and the monitor lays her eggs in this chamber, then she trots on her way. The termites go to work at once to repair their nest, patching the hole. The patch soon becomes as rock hard as the rest of the tall, boulderlike nest. Thus, the monitor eggs are perfectly protected and also get the heat they need for hatching inside the sun-baked nest. When the eggs hatch after about 5 months, the babies break open the shells and a watery fluid trickles out. This fluid softens the nest wall again—and the baby monitors easily dig their way out with their sharp claws.

Monitors are an old reptile family that dates back to the days of the dinosaurs, at least 70 million years ago. One relative of the monitor family that lived at that time was *truly* a giant lizard; *Mososaurus,* a monitorlike lizard that lived in the sea, was 35 feet long!

Nile Monitors Raiding a Crocodile's Nest

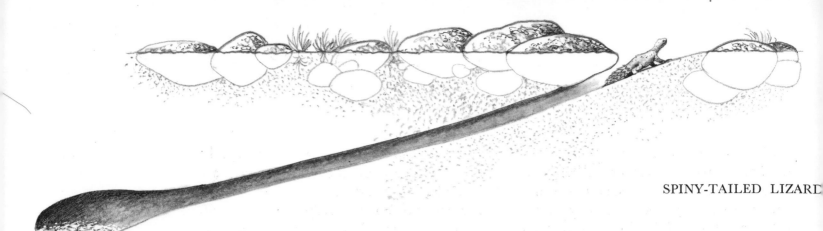

The Desert Dweller—DEFENSE IS BEST

THE LIZARD was crouched in its dwelling, a 9-foot-long tunnel beneath the ground. It had dug the tunnel itself, with its sharp claws. It spent its nights here, underground, safe from the chill that came with darkness and the many dangerous creatures that prowled the night. But now the lizard could sense that the sun had risen and that the desert overhead was rapidly warming. Time to soak up some warmth and then go in search of food. The lizard crept up the tunnel, pushed aside the plug of sand with which it had blocked the entrance the evening before, and emerged into the early morning sunlight.

The lizard was a heavy-bodied reptile, about a foot long, with stout legs and a thick, stubby tail ringed with rows of spikes. This tail gave the lizard the name by which humans call it—spiny-tailed lizard. With such a wicked-appearing tail and the rather frowning appearance of its blunt head, the lizard looked as if it might be a fierce animal, but actually it was a gentle creature. It ate only the grass, leaves, flowers, and fruit found in its desert domain. As for water, it seldom if ever drank, for there was little water to be had. It got all the moisture it needed from the juices of the plants it ate.

Picking out a spot not far from its hole, the lizard settled itself for a sunbath, stretching out its front legs and tilting its body to expose as much as possible of itself to the sun's rays. The lizard's color was a dark khaki brown, but as it began to warm up, this color lightened. When the lizard grew warm enough, its body would be a yellowish color, which would not allow it to take in as much sunlight.

But the lizard was about to have its sunbath interrupted. Another desert dweller had come into sight—a large snake, for which the spiny-tailed lizard seemed an ideal breakfast! Like a flash of dark lightning against the tan ground, the snake writhed swiftly toward its intended prey.

Turning quickly, the lizard scuttled straight for its hole. Had it crept down to the bottom, to cower there, it would have been doomed, for the snake easily could have followed it. But the lizard had something else in mind. With its body just inside the entrance, it stopped. Its wicked, spiny tail was sticking out—and the lizard began to wave it vigorously.

The snake paused for a moment; then it made a darting lunge at the waving tail. It received a vicious blow from the spiky club,

knocking it backward! The snake emitted an angry hiss, staring with unwinking eyes at the dangerously lashing tail. After a few moments, it crawled on its way to seek an easier meal elsewhere.

The deserts of the world abound with lizards, which, like the spiny-tailed lizard of North Africa and northern India, have ways of surviving the harshness and dangers of their barren world.

In the rocky desert portions of the southwestern United States and the northwestern corner of Mexico, there lives a fat-bellied, thick-tailed, 16-inch-long lizard known as the chuckwalla. Like the spiny-tailed lizard, it gets its food and water from the leaves and flowers of hardy desert plants. It too basks in the sun to warm its body enough for normal movement and seeks a shadowy shelter when its body grows too warm. But the chuckwalla does not have the spiny-tailed lizard's dangerous tail, so it must defend itself another way. When danger threatens, it scurries to the nearest cluster of boulders and squeezes itself into a narrow space between two of them. Then, it breathes in great gulps of air, filling its lungs until it literally swells up like a balloon, making its body more than half again its regular size. This wedges it so tightly between the rocks that it cannot be pulled out or swallowed by an enemy.

In the deserts of Australia lives the lizard known as the thorny devil or the moloch. This lizard eats ants, which are plentiful in the desert, snapping up 20 or 30 at a lick; it often eats more than a thousand at a single meal. But there is little moisture in the body of an ant, so the moloch must take advantage of whatever water it finds. Its skin, between all its scales, is filled with tiny, threadlike grooves; whenever water touches the moloch's body, the grooves fill up, so that the lizard seems to be soaking up the water. Slowly, then, the moisture trickles down the grooves to the corners of the moloch's mouth, and, to drink, it has only to move its jaws slightly. Thus, this lizard frequently takes a supply of drinking water right along with it.

For defense, the moloch carries the measure of the spiny-tailed lizard a bit farther. Its whole body bristles with sharp spikes, like the thorns on a rosebush. When faced with danger, it bends its head down and arches its round back—it becomes a spiky ball. Although it is only 8 inches long, small enough to be easily swallowed whole, the moloch would make a most prickly and unpleasant mouthful for nearly any creature.

The girdle-tailed lizard of the rocky desert country in southern Africa combines the defenses of the moloch, the spiny-tailed lizard, *and* the chuckwalla. It also throws in a special twist of its own. A girdle-tailed lizard's whole body, except for its belly, is ringed with sharp spikes. If danger threatens, the lizard heads for the nearest rocky crevice, just as a chuckwalla does, and squeezes itself in. Then it coils itself into a circle, holding its tail in its mouth. A snake can't coil around it, and faced with all those spikes no other animal would be willing to seize a mouthful of it to try to pull it out.

Chuckwalla

46

Moloch

Fringe-Toed Lizard

Gila Monster

The girdle-tailed lizard also uses its spiky tail as a club, just as the spiny-tailed lizard does. A scientist once saw one of these lizards caught out in the open by a snake called a puff adder, which began to swallow it headfirst. The lizard struggled valiantly, lashing its tail and beating the snake soundly with it. After a bit of this, the snake "threw up" the lizard's head and fled!

The fringe-toed lizard, which lives in the same part of North America as the chuckwalla, escapes danger by diving headfirst into loose sand and "swimming" out of sight! It really does "swim" much as if it were in water—holding its front legs tight against its body while kicking with its back legs and wiggling its back and tail like a fish in a pond. It is able to vanish into a sand dune with amazing speed. While submerged, it can close off its nostrils and ear openings so sand won't get into them, and its eyes are protected by thick lashes. The fringe on this lizard's toes turns its feet into "snowshoes," enabling it to run across loose sand without sinking in, just as a person wearing snowshoes walks over thick snow.

The pudgy, 2-foot-long Gila monster of the southwestern United States seems to feel that the best defense is an *attack*! It is one of the only two poisonous lizards in the world. While it uses its poison mainly for killing such prey as mice and rabbits, it also uses it in defense. If a Gila monster is threatened, it hisses a warning, then attacks, biting fiercely. As it bites, poison is squirted down through grooves in its teeth. The poison is as deadly as a coral snake's.

The gridiron-tailed lizard of North American deserts is a slim-bodied, perky-looking reptile whose long tail looks as if it has been cooked on a barbeque grill or gridiron. The tail is ringed with several black bands that stand out against the lizard's pale green color. The gridiron-tailed lizard's defense is simply to run away, but it doesn't scurry off on all fours as most lizards do—it "stands up" and runs on its two back legs, much as many of the two-legged dinosaurs must have run. And it moves surprisingly fast—as fast as 15 miles an hour.

As the lizard runs, its black-banded tail waves from side to side. This tail becomes the main target for most animals tempted to chase a gridiron-tailed lizard. And that's the whole "idea"—for, if an animal seizes the eye-catching, black-striped, waving tail, the tail breaks right off the lizard's body, leaving the pursuer with a morsel to eat and enabling the lizard to escape! This trick of shedding tails is one used by a great many kinds of lizards. It doesn't harm the reptile in the least. The tail is actually *constructed* to come off! In time, the lizard grows a new tail, although usually it is shorter than the lost tail. Tail shedding has enabled many a lizard to stay alive!

47

Gridiron-Tailed Lizard

The Tree Dweller—CAMOUFLAGE EXPERT

IT LOOKED like a fantastic, bug-eyed, three-horned monster from another planet, perched on the slender branch of a tree. Its scaled and warty brownish green body was flat, as though slightly squashed from side to side. Three pointed, ringed horns jutted straight out from its head; two at the forehead and a longer one at the snout. Its bulging eyes moved in all directions—*literally* in all directions—for while one eye stared to the right, the other swiveled to look straight up, and when one turned to look down, the other peered straight ahead! The eyes in their round, bulging "turrets" worked separately from one another, giving the creature a kind of vision no human could ever quite imagine!

The creature was a 10-inch-long, tree-dwelling lizard known as a chameleon, and it was the particular kind of chameleon called Jackson's chameleon. Suddenly, its swiveling eyes caught a quick quiver of motion. On a slightly lower branch, some dozen inches away, a large green locust reposed, motionless except for the twitching of its feelers. This movement had caught the chameleon's notice.

Stealthily, the chameleon began to inch forward, curling its long tail around the branch and gripping tightly with each foot. Perhaps the locust was unaware of the predator, for the lizard was moving with infinite slowness. Rocking slightly, its flat body looked surprisingly like a leaf trembling in a light breeze. Or perhaps the lizard had not yet come close enough to alarm the insect. Had the chameleon made a quick rush, the locust would have launched itself into sudden, whirring flight and would probably have gotten away. But there was no need for the chameleon to charge. It had moved near enough for its purpose. Its bulging eyes, now working together, were focused directly on the insect. Its mouth opened slightly, revealing a purple pink bulge, like a wad of chewing gum. There was a sudden blur of pink, and the locust vanished from its branch—to appear in the chameleon's mouth!

The chameleon had used its "secret weapon"—a stretchable tongue with a swollen, sticky tip. A chameleon can shoot this tongue out of its mouth at a speed of 1/16 of a second to a distance greater than the length of its body! The tip will fasten onto almost any food it touches, carrying it back into the lizard's mouth to be crunched up and swallowed. No other kind of reptile

48

Chameleons:

Jackson's

Fisher's

Short-Horned

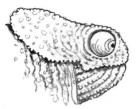

Flap-Necked

has such a tongue as this.

There are about a hundred different kinds of chameleons. Most live in Africa and the big island of Madagascar near Africa, and a few kinds live in Europe and Asia. In general, all look much alike, with bulging eye turrets, flat, high-backed bodies, and long tails. However, some chameleons have a horn, some have two horns, some have three horns, and some have a sort of shield that grows out of the top of the head and slants back over the neck. Some have stubby tails instead of long ones. These lizards range in size from little creatures only a few inches long to "giants" nearly 2 feet long. The giant chameleons can use their shooting tongues to catch small lizards, birds, and even young mice.

Although well known for their ability to change color to hide themselves, chameleons actually cannot change color quite as much as most people believe. Each kind of chameleon has only a few colors to make use of. Some, for example, cannot turn any shade of green; others can't make themselves any shade of red. Chameleons don't change color just for camouflage, either; they may do so when they are angry, frightened, or when the temperature changes. When a Jackson's chameleon basks in the early morning sun, its body is a dark color. This helps it to warm up faster, because dark colors absorb, or soak in, sunlight. But as the chameleon grows warm, its color changes to pale yellow. This helps keep it from becoming any warmer, because light colors do not absorb as much sunlight. They reflect it.

Most chameleons make their homes in trees or bushes, although a few kinds, such as the stubby-tailed ones, are ground dwellers. The tree-dwelling chameleons are perfectly suited to life in the trees. Their toes, instead of being widely separated like the toes of most lizards, are fused, or stuck together, in clusters of two and three; the chameleons' feet form "tweezers" to easily grip slim, round branches. Their tails will not break, like the tails of many other lizards, and are used in exactly the same way that prehensile-tailed monkeys use their tails—to wrap around tree branches and help keep the chameleon from falling.

But chameleons aren't the only lizards suited to life in the trees. A great many members of the lizard "family" are tree dwellers.

In parts of Asia live tree-dwelling, color-changing lizards with the horrifying name of bloodsuckers! They are called this because of the bright red color their heads sometimes take on, not because they actually suck anything's blood. They are slim, long-nosed reptiles about 7 inches long, and they have a fringe of pointed scales sticking up on their necks.

Another group of tree lizards, the angle-headed lizards, also live in Asia. They can change color so quickly, to blend in with their surroundings, that they are hard to see and hard to find. Rather fierce-looking reptiles, each has a row of pointed, spiky scales running down its back and tail and a large, rounded piece of skin, like a bag, hanging from its lower jaw.

But of all the tree-dwelling lizards, per-

haps the strangest are the little creatures called flying dragons. They are the closest thing in the world today to a *flying* reptile.

About 15 kinds of these lizards live in forests in several parts of Southeast Asia. When seen resting, a flying dragon looks like an ordinary slim lizard, 8 to 12 inches long. The fact is it's very hard *to* see when it clings motionless to a tree trunk, for its grayish brown body looks just like tree bark. Then, suddenly, it may launch itself into the air and go sailing with outstretched wings to another tree 30 or 40 feet away!

The "wings" aren't really wings, however. They're rounded webs of scaly skin stretched over long, slender ribs, and they stick out from each side of the lizard's body, between its front and back legs, when it flies. The lizard cannot flap these wings, so it is really a glider, not a flier. The wings lay folded flat against its body until it "takes off." Several kinds of flying dragons have beautifully colored wings—orange with black spots, or purple black with pale spots. The wings flutter as the flying

dragons glide, and the creatures look like big butterflies darting from tree to tree.

Flying dragons go from one tree to another to feed. They land right on a tree's trunk, rather than on a branch as a bird does, digging into the bark with all four feet. Then they go scampering up the trunk, snapping up any small insects they encounter. They prefer ants. When a flying dragon reaches the top of a tree, off it goes in flight to another tree. Or it may bask for a while in the bright sunlight among the tree's top branches, or cling to the trunk disguised as a piece of bark. About the only time a flying dragon ever leaves the trees is when a female comes down to the ground to dig a hole and lay her eggs in it.

It's interesting that one of the oldest prehistoric lizards we know of—a creature called *Kuehneosaurus* of about 200 million years ago—apparently had "wings" much like those of today's flying dragons, so it must have been a tree dweller, too. It looks as if lizards have been living in trees for a long, long time!

Flying Dragons

The Glass Snake—LIZARD WITHOUT LEGS

THE CREATURE moving slowly through the damp grass of the field seemed to be a snake. But there was something peculiar about it. It didn't crawl with the smooth, gliding motion most snakes have; it seemed stiff and clumsy. And from time to time it could be seen distinctly to blink its eyes. But snakes never blink! What sort of snake *was* this crawling creature?

The red fox stealthily stalking the creature didn't care in the slightest what it was. To the fox, it represented a meal. With a quick rush, the fox pounced.

As it did so, something strange happened. The crawling creature's tail literally *broke* into several pieces that twitched and squirmed as if each had a life of its own! Momentarily puzzled, the fox stared from one to another. Meanwhile, the front end of the creature, moving as quickly as it could, crawled out of sight.

The reptile that had lost its tail to the fox wasn't a snake at all. It was a lizard that looks like a snake. Inasmuch as a snake is just a lizard without legs, you may wonder what the difference is between a snake and a lizard that looks like a snake. Well, there are at least two big differences.

Snakes don't have eyelids. Their eyes are covered by transparent skin. Thus, a snake can never blink or close its eyes at all, even when it sleeps. The lizard that looks like a snake has eyelids to blink and to close its eyes to sleep.

The other major difference is that, like many lizards, the lizard that looks like a snake can lose its tail and grow a new one. No snake in the world can do this trick.

This snakelike lizard is called a glass snake, because of the way its tail seems to shatter like glass. The purpose of such a tail is, of course, to help the lizard survive. While a bird or mammal is trying to gobble up its pieces of tail, the glass snake, which now isn't much bigger than one of the pieces, makes its getaway.

An old legend says that a glass snake can put the pieces of itself back together, but this isn't true. A glass snake can only grow a new tail, and the new one is never as long as the one that broke off.

A glass snake is not as limber and agile as a snake. A snake in a hurry *flows* smoothly over the ground with a rapid in-and-out curving of its body. But a glass snake sort of twists along, having to stop and rest for a moment every 2 or 3 yards. A glass snake can't climb trees, and it doesn't swim. Many

52

snakes both swim and climb trees.

Glass snakes live in open fields and in bare, rocky places. They aren't a bit rare. Three kinds live in North America, and one, which is about 3 feet long, is actually the longest lizard in the United States. Other glass snakes live in Europe, Asia Minor, China, India, and North Africa.

The biggest member of this snaky lizard group lives in Yugoslavia, southern Russia, and other parts of southeastern Europe. It is about 4 feet long and as thick around as a man's wrist. It has a brown back and a yellowish underside, which is why it is known as the *sheltopusik,* a Slavic word meaning "yellow belly." The sheltopusik isn't truly legless; it has two tiny stubs, the size of warts, midway down its body.

American glass snakes eat mostly spiders and insects, but the bigger sheltopusik hunts snails, mice, and sometimes even small lizards. A snake seizes its prey and swallows it smoothly down. A glass snake such as the sheltopusik twists its prey around and around, beats it on the ground to stun it, then chomps on it with powerful jaws and finally swallows it whole. It gobbles snails, shells and all. Once in a while a sheltopusik may feast on bird or snake eggs. It cracks them open and slurps out the insides with its tongue.

In England there are cousins of the glass snakes known as slow worms. These, too, look like snakes rather than worms. They got their name because they usually move quite slowly, as if deciding just what to do. However, they can move rather fast when they want to.

Most slow worms are about a foot long. Like glass snakes, they live in open fields or in wooded areas where the trees are far apart. They hide under stones or logs during the day and usually come out after sundown to hunt. They eat spiders and worms, but mainly they eat slugs, which makes them a good friend to farmers and gardeners, for slugs do a great deal of damage to many vegetables. When a slow worm finds a slug, it grabs it by the middle and chews it from end to end with sharp, curving teeth that easily hold the slippery creature.

But even though slow worms are good friends to humans, humans are just about the slow worm's worst enemy. Many people who see a snakelike creature seem to think it must be poisonous, and they try to kill it. Thousands of useful slow worms and glass snakes are killed by people. They are also preyed upon by animals—rats, foxes, owls, buzzards, large lizards, and snakes.

Slow worms give birth to young that leave their mother's body in a kind of jellylike envelope. The babies, which are about 3 inches long, tear their way out and then are on their own. They are able to look after themselves quite well and soon go hunting for insects and small slugs. Glass snakes lay eggs, and one kind of American glass snake protects her eggs after she lays them by encircling them with her body.

Glass snakes and slow worms look like snakes, but the reptiles called worm lizards really do look just like big worms. Their bodies are blunt at both ends and divided into many rings, just as an earthworm's body is. They have tiny eyes, and, of course,

54

Sheltopusik

most have no legs. They even live much as earthworms do, tunneling through the ground and seldom coming up into daylight. When they do crawl on the ground, they don't wiggle from side to side as a snake does, or twist like a glass snake, but move in a straight line in wormlike fashion. However—like glass snakes, slow worms, and many other lizards—some worm lizards have tails that break off and wiggle if seized by an enemy.

Most worm lizards are about a foot long. They dig networks of tunnels with their shovel-shaped heads, carefully packing the soil tightly onto the tunnel walls. They can crawl either forward or backward through their tunnels, listening for the sounds of insects moving in the ground nearby. Their main foods are ants and termites. The lizards tunnel into the nests of these insects and then proceed to use the nests as both restaurants and nursuries, laying their eggs in the nests and feeding on the swarming insects. Ants and termites have vicious, biting jaws, but their bites don't seem to bother the worm lizards. Because worm lizards are so often found in ant nests, these reptiles are known as "ant kings" in parts of South America, where some people believe the ants raise and feed them.

Not all worm lizards are legless. Three kinds in lower California have short, stubby front legs with five-fingered "hands." Imagine a long, fat earthworm with two little front feet and you'll understand how odd these creatures look.

Glass snakes, slow worms, and worm lizards aren't the only lizards to have lost all or some legs in evolution. A number of other lizards either have no legs or, like the lizard called a sand skink, have pairs of tiny, useless limbs placed far apart from one another on the creature's snakelike body. A sand skink cannot use its tiny legs at all—it crawls like a snake. Chances are, many millions of years from now, the sand skink's descendants will have lost their legs completely and will look much like glass snakes. It really seems as if many kinds of lizards have "decided" that there's no real advantage to having legs, and they're quite satisfied to do without them!

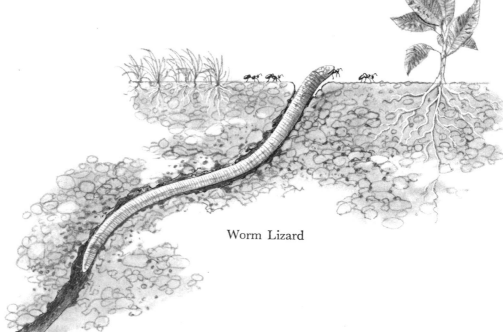

Worm Lizard

The Tuatara—UNIQUE AND PRIMITIVE

NEAR THE BIG South Island of New Zealand in the Pacific Ocean, there lies a tiny, steep, rocky island—the top of an underwater mountain. The upper part of this island, above the rocky cliffs, is covered with soil in which grows coarse grass dotted with boulders. If you were to walk about in the grass, you would discover a large number of holes, often tucked away beneath the edge of a boulder. These holes were dug by small gray and white birds called dovey petrels. The holes are the birds' nests.

If you dug open one of the nests, you would probably find a mother petrel, perhaps snuggled down with a single fuzzy, dark gray chick. And you would probably find something else rather surprising—a strange houseguest. In many of these holes, living right with the petrel family, there will be a small, pudgy, dull yellowish or olive brown *reptile*.

This reptile sharing the home of a bird has the scientific name of *Sphenodon*, which means "wedge tooth." But the Maori people, who were the first people to settle in New Zealand, were the ones to give the little animal the name by which it is now best known—tuatara. In the Maori language

that means something like "having spines" and was given because of the row of little white spikes that look like teeth running down the reptile's back. Actually these are elongated scales called spines.

The tuatara looks like one of the many kinds of lizards that inhabit the world today. But it isn't a lizard at all; it's really a very special one-of-a-kind creature! Its body is different in several ways from the bodies of other reptiles, and its brain is no bigger than a pea. It is a *primitive* reptile, like the reptiles of more than 220 million years ago!

At that time, before there were any turtles, lizards, snakes, or crocodilians, and even before the first dinosaurs had come into the world, there was a big group of reptiles that have been named *Rhynchocephalians* or "beak heads." And one kind of beak head was the creature we now call a tuatara! All the others have become extinct, just as the dinosaurs have, but the tuatara somehow survived. It is one of the oldest kinds of living reptiles—a creature that probably still lives in much the same way many kinds of reptiles did 200 million years ago. This makes it a fascinating animal to study, for scientists and anyone

Dovey Petrel
TUATARA

interested in trying to figure out how pre-historic animals may have lived.

Some of the beak heads of 200 million years ago were as much as 6 feet long, but tuataras are only about 2 feet long. Although tuataras often share the underground burrows of the petrels, they can dig burrows for themselves and often do. They dig as a dog does, using their five-fingered front feet, which look like the hands of a fat baby, to fling out the earth in a shower behind them. When their digging is complete, they line the burrows with dried leaves and grass. The reptiles live alone in these holes, spending the days down inside them, except for in the morning and evening when they crouch in the burrow entrance to bask in the sun awhile.

When the darkness of night covers the island, the tuataras come out to hunt. A tuatara routed from its burrow in the daytime or captive in a zoo is a slow-moving creature that may hardly seem to be breathing, but a wild tuatara at night is quick and active. This is surprising, for nights on the island can be quite chilly—as low as 45 degrees, a temperature which would cause most reptiles to become numb with cold and unable to move well. But the tuatara doesn't seem to mind this low temperature a bit. Some scientists think the world may have been rather cool about the time the Rhynchocephalians appeared.

The tuataras hunt mainly beetles, spiders, and the 3-inch-long grasshopperlike insects known as wetas in New Zealand. They also enjoy earthworms, slugs, and snails and will gobble up bird eggs and baby birds, as well

as small lizards. They creep up on their prey and seize it with a sudden lunge. Unlike many reptiles, which swallow their prey whole or tear off pieces and gulp them down, tuataras chew their food, often for as long as several minutes.

An odd thing about the tuatara is that it has *three* eyes, although only two—the ones on each side of its head—actually work. The third eye is up on top of the tuatara's head, and it's really just a lens covered over with skin. However, a nerve connects the lens to the tuatara's brain, and perhaps very long ago, the ancestors of tuataras had a third eye actually able to see. (A number of lizards also have third "eyes" of this sort, too.)

The tuatara also has three *eyelids* on its working eyes. Two are lids that close from top to bottom, like a lizard's eyelids and like yours. But the third slides up from a corner of the tuatara's eye, "wiping off" the eyeball from time to time, then slides back. Lizards do not have such an eyelid, but crocodilians do.

Like most reptiles, tuataras lay eggs. A mother tuatara digs a hole about 5 inches deep in the earth and lays from 8 to 15 leathery-shelled eggs in it. Then she covers them up and goes on her way, leaving the eggs to hatch on their own. But, unlike the eggs of most reptiles, which hatch in a matter of months or weeks, tuatara eggs do not hatch for a year or more. The baby tuataras are brownish pink in color and about 4½ inches long. They dig their way to the surface and begin to hunt for food. They grow very slowly—and keep growing until they are about 50 years old! It is thought that tuataras probably live to be a hundred or more.

Within the last hundred years, tuataras were in serious danger of becoming extinct, which would have been a sad thing after surviving for so many millions of years. The danger, once again, was from people. Many tuataras once lived in New Zealand, where they had no trouble existing for millions of years. But during the last two hundred years, more and more people have settled in New Zealand, bringing with them cats, dogs, pigs, and many other animals foreign to the islands—animals against which the little tuataras had no defense. The dogs, cats, and pigs were easily able to catch and eat the slower moving tuataras. To make matters worse, herds of sheep were brought to New Zealand, and the sheep grazed on the great fields of grass where the tuataras

did most of their hunting for insects. This drove away most of the insects, and there was no longer enough food for the tuataras. Sometime between 150 and 100 years ago, all the tuataras on New Zealand died out.

Only a few were left on some of the small islands nearby. But they were in danger, too. Fortunately, the government of New Zealand, through the efforts of scientists, declared the islands as places of refuge for the tuataras. Humans may not live on, nor, except for scientists, visit the islands, and "foreign" animals are kept off them. And so the little reptiles were saved. There are probably about ten thousand of them left, living in safety on their protected islands—unique animals that have hardly changed since the days before the dinosaurs. The tuataras show us what many of the reptiles of 200 million years ago must have been like.

Index

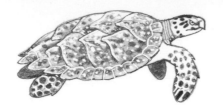

PRINTED IN U.S.A.

Pronunciation Guide

amethystine	(am-uh-THIS-tuhn)
anaconda	(an-uh-KAHN-duh)
ankylosaur	(ANG-kih-loh-SAWR)
Boidae	(BOH-eh-day)
caiman	(KAY-man)
chameleon	(kuh-MEEL-yuhn)
Chelonia	(keh-LOH-nee-uh)
Corythosaurus	(kuh-RITH-uh-SAW-ruhs)
Crocodilia	(KRAH-kuh-DIL-ee-yuh)
Elapid	(ee-LAY-pid)
Galapagos	(guh-LAHP-uh-guhs)
gavial	(GAY-vee-ul)
Gila	(HEE-luh)
Icthyostega	(IK-thee-oh-STAY-guh)
Komodo	(kuh-MOH-doh)
Kuehneosaurus	(KUE-nee-oh-SAW-ruhs)
Maori	(MAH-oh-ree)
moloch	(MOH-lahk)
Mososaurus	(MOH-suh-SAW-ruhs)
Phobosuchus	(foh-boh-SOOK-uhs)
reticulated	(reh-TIK-yuh-LAYT-ed)
Romeriscus	(ROH-muhr-IS-kuhs)
Rhynchocephalia	(RING-koh-suh-FAYL-yuh)
sheltopusik	(SHEL-toh-POOS-ik)
Sphenodon	(SFEE-noh-dahn)
Squamata	(skwah-MAY-tuh)
Stegosaurus	(STEG-uh-SAW-ruhs)
tuatara	(too-uh-TAH-ruh)
weta	(WAY-tah)

61

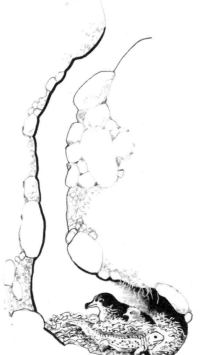